LOVE IS...

WALKING HAND-IN-HAND

BY CHARLES M. SCHULZ

First published in this edition 1982
Published by William Collins Sons and Co Ltd, London and Glasgow

Copyright © 1979 by United Feature Syndicate, Inc.
All rights reserved
Based on "Love is Walking Hand-in-Hand"
by Charles M. Schulz
(Copyright © 1965 by United Feature Syndicate, Inc.)
Printed in Hong Kong by South China Printing Co
ISBN 0-00-195319-2

Charles M. Schulz, creator of Snoopy and the entire *PEANUTS*® gang is now world famous. The humour of his words and drawings is unique; its appeal is universal.

The first edition of LOVE IS WALKING HAND-IN-HAND appeared in 1965 and was an immediate success. This new enlarged version all in colour contains three times as many pages, full of new drawings, new sentiments, new fun – new *Love*.

Another book by Charles M. Schulz, HAPPINESS IS A WARM PUPPY came out in 1962 and is also available in a new enlarged edition.

Love is having a special song.

Love is
accepting
a person
for what
he is.

Love is
sharing your
popcorn.

Love is
getting someone
a glass of water
in the middle
of the night.

Love is
a valentine
with lace
all around
the edges.

Love is looking out for your friends.

Love is
a phone call.

Love is a helping hand.

Love is
trust.

Love is
being
nominated
neighborhood
dog of the
year.

Love is
eating out with
your whole
family.

Love is rooting together for your team.

Love is wanting to make someone smile.

Love is
listening
without
interrupting.

Love is being polite to people.

Love is helping your team to win.

Love is
visiting
a sick friend.

Love is
watching
someone else's
boring show
on T.V.

Love is
sitting
all the way
through
a recital.

Love is believing in someone.

Love is
not littering.

Love is helping someone through his battles.

Love is
hoping that
she hasn't
forgotten
you.

Love is
walking
in the rain
together.

Love is making fudge together.

Love is
flowers from
your favorite
person.

Love is
being
tolerant.

Love is
meeting someone
by the pencil
sharpener.

Love is
letting your
house guest
have your
room.

Love is waking someone up from a bad dream.

Love is making plans together.

Love is
wondering
what he's doing
right now this
very moment.

Love is being a good loser.

Love is
buying somebody
a present
with your
own money.

Love is
passing notes
back and forth
in school.

Love is being hospitable.

Love is
letting him win
even though you
know you could
slaughter
him.

Love is
being happy
just knowing
that she's happy...
but that
isn't so easy.

Love is dressing up for someone.

Love is
a push
in the right
direction.

Love is
not nagging.

Love is being faithful to the very end.

Love is
when your friends
ask to give you
a testimonial
dinner.

Love is tickling.

Love is
an invitation
to lunch.

Love is allowing someone to sleep late.

Love is committing yourself in writing.

Love is hating to say goodbye.

Love is
mussing up
someone's
hair.

Love is
loaning your
best comic
magazines.

Love is
walking
hand-in-hand.

Love is helping your sister with her homework.

Love is
a letter
on pink
stationery.

Love is
being a good
watch dog.

Love is
wishing you had
nerve enough
to go over
and talk with
that little girl
with the
red hair.

Love is being patient with your little brother.

Love is
close
dancing.

Love is standing in a doorway just to see her if she comes walking by.

Love is
a flag.

Love is
a goodnight
kiss.

Love is
a smile
even when
he keeps you
waiting.

Love is
the whole
world.